nature spots
IN THE COUNTRY

There are 80 **Nature** Spots for you to find in the countryside. Each time you find one you earn a bronze, silver or gold medal.

There are nine different places to look for **Nature** Spots...

Hedgerow birds	page **2**	Mammal tracks	**34**
Hedgerow trees	**6**	Mammal burrows	**36**
Wayside flowers	**12**	Mammal droppings	**39**
Marvellous mammals	**24**	Looking for ladybirds	**42**
Signs of squirrels	**30**		

 BRONZE targets are easy to find in most gardens.

 SILVER targets need some detective work.

 GOLD targets are hard to find but not impossible!

Hedgerow birds

You don't need any special equipment to spot these birds. A great place to start is exploring hedgerows. The best hedges for birds have plenty of cover, so are tall and bushy.

Birds fly into hedges to look for food and somewhere to build a nest. **Think like a bird – where would you go?**

1. Robin

What to look for

Orange-red breast. Light brown head. Grey or white underside. Flicking flight.

Where to look

Common in fields and hedges. Often seen hunting for insects on newly dug soil.

When to see it

All year round.

Date seen:

2. Blackbird

male

What to look for

Male is all black, with an orange-yellow bill and ring around each eye. Female is dark brown. Young birds are speckled brown.

Where to look

Very common in fields and hedges. Often seen hopping and running over grass.

When to see it

All year round.

Date seen:

3. Song thrush

What to look for

Brown back. Speckled white breast. Pale orange patch on underwing. Smaller than a blackbird.

Where to look

Seen around hedges. Does not often move far from cover.

When to see it

All year round.

Date seen:

4. Wren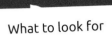

What to look for

Very small brown bird. Fat body. Short rounded wings. Tail is sometimes pointing up. They are one of the loudest song birds, despite their small size.

Where to look

Hedges and woods, often close to the ground.

When to see it

All year round.

Date seen:

5. Chaffinch

male

What to look for

Male with blue-grey head and pink underneath. Stout bill.

Where to look

Widespread along hedges, in woods and in gardens. Often seen feeding on the ground.

When to see it

All year round.

Date seen:

6. Greenfinch

What to look for

Dull green body. Yellow flashes on wings and tail. Tail is forked. Stout pale bill.

Where to look

Look around hedges, trees and bushes.

When to see it

All year round.

Date seen:

7. Long-tailed tit

What to look for

Very long tail. Round body. Black and white with pink patches. Tiny black bill.

Where to look

Watch it flitting between the branches of hedges and trees, sometimes in large family groups.

When to see it

All year round.

Date seen:

Hedgerow trees

A hedge is a line of woody plants that has been shaped into a living fence. You can spot hedgerow trees and shrubs all year round. The leaves, flowers, twigs, buds, berries and nuts are all useful clues.

Many of the woody plants found growing in hedges have lots of thorns. Why do you think this might be?

🔍 A hedgerow is defined as a line of woody plants that have been managed so that the trees and shrubs no longer form their natural shape.

🔍 There are around 300,000 miles of managed hedgerow in Great Britain (CEH Countryside Survey). This is approximately 1.25 times the distance from the Earth to the Moon.

🔍 Old hedges have the greatest mix of different woody plants. Try looking at the hedges near to churches and churchyards, old villages and along winding country lanes. Where has the highest number of woody plants?

8. Hawthorn

What to look for

White flower in spring. Very thorny. If it is not cut, it grows into a small tree. Leaves with 3-5 deep lobes. Red berries (*haws*) in autumn.

Where to look

Very common in hedgerows.

When to see it

Flowers May to June at the same time as the leaves appear.

Date seen:

9. Blackthorn

What to look for

White flower. Spiny shrub or small tree. Leaves rounded, not lobed but edges toothed. Blue-black fruit (*sloes*) in autumn.

Where to look

Throughout Great Britain and Ireland.

When to see it

Flowers March to April, before the leaves appear.

Date seen:

10. Elder

What to look for
Creamy white flowers in a dense flowerhead. The bark is deeply furrowed and may look like cork.

Where to look
Hedges and waste ground.

When to see it
Flowers May to June. Black fruit produced in drooping bunches from August to September.

Date seen:

11. Hazel

What to look for
Oval leaves with toothed edges. Leaves feel soft and downy. Bark shiny grey or brown. The flowers are yellow-green catkins.

Where to look
Common in hedgerows.

When to see it
Catkins January to March. Nuts September to October.

Date seen:

12. Holly

What to look for

Leaves stiff and waxy, with spiny teeth. Small white flowers. Red berries. Bark dull grey, often warty.

Where to look

Common throughout Great Britain and Ireland.

When to see it

Evergreen. Flowers from May to August. Fruit in autumn and winter.

Date seen:

13. Field maple

What to look for

Leaf with 3 lobes. Lobes blunt and rounded. Leaf stem green, releases latex when cut. Seed shaped like a propeller, with horizontal wings. Green-yellow flowers, held upright.

Where to look

Often found in hedges.

When to see it

Flowers May to June.

Date seen:

14. Dog rose

What to look for

Pink or white flowers. 5 lobed petals. Stems with prickles. Leaves divided into 3 or 5 leaflets. Fruit (*rose hips*) following the flowers.

Where to look

Hedgerows, waste ground, woodland.

When to see it

Flowers June to July.

Date seen:

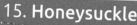

15. Honeysuckle

What to look for

White, yellow or purple flowers, trumpet-shaped with two lips. Fragrant. Cluster of red berries afterwards. Up to 6 m high.

Where to look

A woody climbing plant, common along hedgerows and in woodlands.

When to see it

Flowers June to September.

Date seen:

16. Ivy

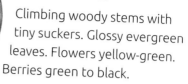

What to look for

Climbing woody stems with tiny suckers. Glossy evergreen leaves. Flowers yellow-green. Berries green to black.

Where to look

Common in shady places, including hedgerows and woods.

When to see it

Evergreen. Flowers September to November.

Date seen:

17. Bramble

What to look for

Scrambling woody stem, with many hooked thorns. Flowers with 5 white (or pink) petals. Look for blackberry fruits in autumn.

Where to look

Common throughout Great Britain and Ireland.

When to see it

Evergreen. All year round.

Date seen:

Wayside flowers

A country walk is a good chance to spot wild flowers. Plan a walk along as many different types of path as you can, like country lanes, canal towpaths and tracks through woodland.

Make a note of how many different wild flowers you find by each type of path. Which path has the highest number?

18. Cow parsley

What to look for

White flower. Finely divided, feather-like leaves.

Where to look

The leaves are found close to the ground in short grass. Flowers mainly found in long grass.

When to see it

Flowers June to August.

Date seen:

19. Greater stitchwort

What to look for

White flower. 5 petals.
Each petal deeply notched.
Yellow stamens. Thin flower
stalks.

Where to look

Hedgerows and woodland.

When to see it

Flowers April to June.

Date seen:

20. Garlic mustard

What to look for

White flowers. 4 petals.
Flowers arranged in clusters.
Leaves similar shape to nettles.
Crushed leaves smell of garlic.

Where to look

Hedgerows, waste ground and
woodland.

When to see it

Flowers April to June.

Date seen:

21. Red campion

What to look for

Red or pink flower. 5 petals. Each petal deeply notched. Slightly hairy.

Where to look

Hedgerows, grassy road verges, woodland paths and woodland edge.

When to see it

Flowers May to September.

Date seen:

22. Foxglove

What to look for

Pink, purple or white flower. Tall spike of bell- shaped flowers. Rosette of hairy leaves.

Where to look

Hedgerows, grassy road verges, woodland paths and woodland edge.

When to see it

Flowers May to October.

Date seen:

23. Rosebay willowherb

What to look for
Pink flower. 4 petals. Tall spike of flowers at top of stem. Long narrow leaves arranged in a spiral up the stem.

Where to look
Grassy road verges, woodland edges, cleared woodland and wasteland.

When to see it
Flowers June to September.

Date seen:

24. Greater willowherb

What to look for
Pink or purple flower. 4 petals. Each petal notched. Softly hairy leaves and stem.

Where to look
Damp grassy places, like ditches and riverbanks.

When to see it
Flowers July to August.

Date seen:

25. Red dead-nettle

What to look for

Pink or purple flowers. Flower divided into two parts: bottom lip and upper hood. Leaves look like nettles, but do not sting.

Where to look

Hedgerows and road verges.

When to see it

Flowers February to November.

Date seen:

26. White dead-nettle

What to look for

White flowers. Flower divided into two parts: bottom lip and upper hood. Leaves look like nettles, but do not sting.

Where to look

Hedgerows and road verges.

When to see it

Flowers March to November.

Date seen:

27. Hedge woundwort

What to look for

Purple flowers. Flower divided into two parts: large bottom lip and smaller upper hood. Leaves have a sharp musty smell, especially when crushed.

Where to look

Shady places under hedges and on grassy banks.

When to see it

Flowers June to August.

Date seen:

28. Hedge bindweed

What to look for

Large white trumpet-shaped flowers. A climbing plant with narrow twisting stems. Leaves arrow-shaped.

Where to look

Hedgerows, ditches, woodland.

When to see it

Flowers June to September.

Date seen:

29. Gorse

What to look for

Yellow flowers. Flower divided into two parts: upper lip and lower lip. A prickly plant with woody branches. Evergreen. Flowers smell of coconut.

Where to look

Grassy places, especially dry and free-draining soils.

When to see it

Flowers all year round.

Date seen:

30. Broom

What to look for

Yellow flowers. No prickles. Long green stems with 5 sides. Older stems are woody. Loses its leaves in winter. No smell.

Where to look

Grassy places, especially dry and free-draining soils.

When to see it

Flowers April to June.

Date seen:

31. Bird's-foot trefoil

What to look for

Yellow flowers, tinged with red. Flowerhead is a group of 2-7 flowers at the top of a long stalk. A low-growing, creeping plant.

Where to look

Dry grassy places throughout Great Britain and Ireland.

When to see it

Flowers June to September.

Date seen:

32. Primrose

What to look for

5 notched yellow petals. Only one flower at the end of each flower-stalk. Rosette of leaves, wrinkled, hairy underneath.

Where to look

Woodland and road verges. Common throughout Great Britain and Ireland.

When to see it

Flowers March to June.

Date seen:

33. Common vetch

What to look for

Pink flower. Flowers in groups of 1-3. A scrambling plant with curly tendrils at the top of the leaf stem.

Where to look

Grassy places like road verges. It can survive in long grass.

When to see it

Flowers May to September.

Date seen:

34. Tufted vetch

What to look for

Blue or purple flower. Flower spike with 10-40 flowers. A scrambling plant with curly tendrils at the top of the leaf stem.

Where to look

Grassy places like road verges. It can survive in long grass.

When to see it

Flowers June to August.

Date seen:

35. Bittersweet

What to look for

Purple and yellow flowers. Weak scrambling stems. Oval-shaped berries, may be green, yellow or red. Also called woody nightshade. **NOTE: the whole plant is poisonous.**

Where to look

Hedgerows.

When to see it

Flowers June to September.

Date seen:

36. Scabious

What to look for

Pale blue semi-circular flowerhead at top of stem. 3 different species: small scabious, field scabious and devil's-bit scabious.

Where to look

Grassy places, especially sunny banks.

When to see it

Flowers June to September.

Date seen:

37. Herb robert

What to look for

Pink flower, 5 petals. Leaves triangular in outline, strong smell. Stem and leaves are sometimes tinged with red.

Where to look

Grassy places and bare soil, often in dry places.

When to see it

Flowers May to September.

Date seen:

38. Shining crane's-bill

What to look for

Pink flower, 5 petals. Leaves round in outline, split into lobes and with blunt teeth. Leaves are bright and glossy, and sometimes tinged with red.

Where to look

Grassy places and walls, especially on limestone.

When to see it

Flowers May to August.

Date seen:

39. Cut-leaved crane's-bill

What to look for

Tiny pink flowers (2 mm across).
5 Deeply notched petals.
Leaves divided into lobes
almost to the base.

Where to look

Grassy places, road verges,
fields of crops.

When to see it

Flowers May to August.

Date seen:

40. Hedgerow crane's-bill

What to look for

Large purple flowers
(2 cm across). 5 notched petals.
Leaves round in outline, hairy,
notched about half-way to
centre.

Where to look

Grassy places, especially sunny
banks.

When to see it

Flowers June to August.

Date seen:

Marvellous mammals

Although there are over 5,000 mammal species in the world, only around 60 species live in the wild in Great Britain, and only around 30 species live in the wild in Ireland.

Many mammals are much more active at night than during the day. You can sometimes tell that animals are present by looking for *field signs*, like tracks (pages 34-35), nests (see pages 36-38) and droppings (see pages 39-41).

Don't touch or pick up wild mammals.

Rabbits are the easiest of these mammals to find during the day.

Early morning or late evening is the best time to see foxes, hares, deer and badgers in the open.

Mice, voles and shrews can be common in long grassland and places overgrown with brambles. Sometimes you can hear squeaking. These rodents are often caught alive by cats.

Try going for a walk in woodland after dark. You may see badgers, foxes and deer.

Grey squirrels leave lots of field signs. These are covered on pages 30-33.

41. Rabbit

What to look for

Look for the short white tail ('white scut'), especially as the rabbit runs away. The ears are rounded and do not have black tips.

Where to look

Common throughout Great Britain and Ireland, especially in the lowlands.

When to see it

All year round.

Date seen:

42. Hare

What to look for

Long powerful legs. Ears have black tips.

Where to look

Brown hares are widespread in Great Britain but absent from Ireland. Mountain hares are found throughout Ireland, but only uplands in Britain.

When to see it

All year round.

Date seen:

43. Vole

What to look for

Voles have a round face and chubby body. Ears are small and partly hidden in the fur. Short tail. 3 different species.

Where to look

Overgrown places with lots of cover, especially long damp grass.

When to see it

All year round.

Date seen:

44. Shrew

What to look for

Shrews have long pointed noses. They are very small (under 10 cm long). Short tail. 3 different species.

Where to look

Hedgerows, fields and in leaf litter in woodlands. Only pygmy shrews are found in Ireland.

When to see it

All year round.

Date seen:

45. Mouse

What to look for

Mice have a pointed face with large ears and eyes. The tail is long, sometimes longer than the body. 4 different species.

Where to look

Widespread throughout Great Britain and Ireland.

When to see it

All year round.

Date seen:

46. Hedgehog

What to look for

The only animal with a spiny coat living in the wild in Great Britain and Ireland.

Where to look

Farmland, woodland and gardens. Most active at night. Young or sickly animals may be seen in the daytime.

When to see it

April to September.

Date seen:

47. Fox

What to look for

Looks like a slim dog. Red-brown coat. Bushy tail, often with a white tip.

Where to look

Widespread throughout Great Britain and Ireland. Most often seen early in the morning or late in the evening. Noisy in winter.

When to see it

All year round.

Date seen:

48. Badger

What to look for

Looks like a fat dog with short legs. Black and white striped head, white tipped ears, black body.

Where to look

Widespread in woodland and gardens. Active at dusk and at night. Throughout Great Britain and Ireland.

When to see it

Resident all year round.

Date seen:

49. Deer

What to look for
4 long legs. Size varies from the same as a large dog to a small horse. Sometimes has antlers. Many species.

Where to look
Woodland. Sometimes seen running across paths, especially early morning or late evening.

When to see it
All year round.

Date seen:

50. Stoat

What to look for
Size of a rat. Stoats streak across the road, with a long body that bounds up and down. Black tip on tail.

Where to look
Along hedges, walls and fences, especially where there are lots of rabbits.

When to see it
All year round.

Date seen:

Signs of squirrels

Grey squirrels can be found throughout Great Britain and Ireland. They live in parks and gardens, even in the middle of cities. Red squirrels are only found in a few places.

Even if you can't see them, squirrels leave plenty of signs behind them. Not everyone likes grey squirrels. Why not?

51. Grey squirrel

What to look for

Grey fur, sometimes streaked brown. Bushy tail. Red squirrels have larger ear tufts.

Where to look

Common throughout Great Britain and Ireland, except Scottish Highlands.

When to see it

All year round, including mild days in winter.

Date seen:

52. Squirrel drey

What to look for

The nest of a squirrel is called a *drey*. It has a round shape and is up to 60 cm across. The inner nest is surrounded by twigs and dry leaves.

Where to look

High in trees, in the fork between two branches.

When to see it

Easiest to see in winter.

Date seen:

53. Squirrel footprint

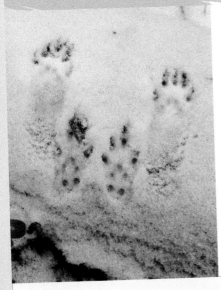

What to look for

Front foot with 4 toes. Back foot with 5 toes. On the back foot, the 3 middle toes are long, straight and narrow.

Where to look

Muddy ground or fresh snow. Tracks may lead down from a tree tunk.

When to see it

All year round.

Date seen:

54. Stripped bark

What to look for

Bark stripped from the trunk or branches, exposing lighter wood underneath.

Where to look

High up in thin-barked trees like beech, sycamore, pine and larch (too high for deer). Often young trees.

When to see it

All year round.

Date seen:

55. Stripped pine cone

What to look for

Cone with some or all of the scales stripped off by the jaws of a squirrel.

Where to look

Underneath pine and fir trees and other conifers.

When to see it

All year round.

Date seen:

56. Nuts eaten by squirrels

What to look for
Hazel nuts that have been sliced in half or shattered into jagged fragments.

Where to look
Near hazel trees, which grow in the shrub layer of open woodlands, in clearings and at the edge.

When to see it
All year round.

Date seen:

57. Nuts eaten by mice

What to look for
Hazel nuts with a hole gnawed in the side or top. These nuts have been eaten by mice or voles.

Where to look
Near hazel trees, which grow in the shrub layer of open woodlands, in clearings and at the edge.

When to see it
All year round.

Date seen:

Mammal tracks

Time for some real detective work! Tracking animal footprints is exciting, but it can be hard to find a perfect print. Look in fresh snow or in muddy places like wheel ruts.

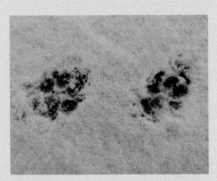

You will find the clearest prints if you go out to look early in the morning (before 10am). Why do you think this is?

58. Dog footprint

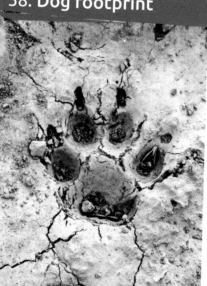

What to look for
A square-shaped pawprint with 4 toes. Claws visible. The palm pad is much larger than the toe pads.

Where to look
Muddy paths throughout.

When to see it
All year round.

Date seen:

59. Fox footprint

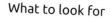

What to look for

Pawprint longer than it is wide. 4 toes. Claws visible. The palm pad is a similar size to the toe pads.

Where to look

Muddy paths along hedgerows and in woodland.

When to see it

All year round.

Date seen:

60. Cat footprint

What to look for

Small pawprint with 4 toes. No claws visible.

Where to look

Muddy places near houses where cats are living.

When to see it

All year round.

Date seen:

Mammal burrows

Many mammals build a refuge, for shelter in winter, and for raising young in summer. The size and shape of the entrance hole to the burrow gives clue to which animal dug it.

If you have found a burrow, but don't know what animal made it, look out for droppings (see pages 39-41).

61. Mole hill

What to look for

Small heap of loose, bare soil. It has been pushed upwards by a mole making tunnels under the ground.

Where to look

Great Britain only. Moles are absent from Ireland. Often found in grassy fields, especially pasture.

When to see it

All year round.

Date seen:

62. Rabbit hole

What to look for

Small round hole (10-20 cm across). Often with piles of rabbit droppings (page 40). Grass is nibbled short near the burrow. There may be patches of bare soil.

Where to look

Grassy fields and hedgerows.

When to see it

All year round.

Date seen:

63. Fox earth

What to look for

Tall and narrow hole (20-25 cm across). Soil that has been dug out forms a fan shape. Often smelly. You may find red-brown hairs just outside the burrow.

Where to look

Woodland and hedgerows.

When to see it

All year round.

Date seen:

64. Badger sett

What to look for
Large semi-circular hole (25-30 cm across). Large mound of compacted soil left at the entrance.

Where to look
Woodland. Often dug on a slope.

When to see it
All year round.

Date seen:

65. Badger hairs

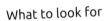

What to look for
Wiry black and white hairs. Badgers use the same path though their territory, so hairs on a fence indicate a badger route.

Where to look
Look at the bottom strand of wire fences near woodland with setts.

When to see it
All year round.

Date seen:

Mammal droppings

You can tell a lot about an animal by the size, shape and smell of its droppings. Don't touch animal droppings with your hands. Instead use a stick to get a closer look inside.

Some animals, like badgers and foxes, leave their droppings in prominent places. Why do you think they do this?

66. Sheep droppings

What to look for

Black. Made up of a mass of cylinder-shaped droppings. Sometimes the droppings are separated.

Where to look

Sheep pasture.

When to see it

All year round.

Date seen:

67. Rabbit droppings

What to look for
Brown or green. Small round droppings, often left in large piles. Each dropping is 1 cm across.

Where to look
Grassy places. Piles of droppings may be left in prominent places like anthills.

When to see it
All year round.

Date seen:

68. Deer droppings

What to look for
Black. Shaped like a short, fat cylinder with a point at one end and a dimple at the other. Larger than rabbit droppings.

Where to look
Woodland, especially the edge of woodland and along woodland paths.

When to see it
All year round.

Date seen:

69. Fox droppings

What to look for

Dark when fresh, grey when old. Unlike dog droppings, fragments of fur, feathers and fruit may be visible. One end is twisted. Smelly.

Where to look

Muddy paths along hedgerows and in woods.

When to see it

All year round.

Date seen:

70. Badger droppings

What to look for

Fat and sausage-shaped or soft and runny. Often left in a shallow pit (called a latrine) close by a sett.

Where to look

Woodland. Look for elder (page 8) and stinging nettles near the setts.

When to see it

All year round.

Date seen:

Looking for ladybirds

There are 26 different species of ladybirds in Great Britain and Ireland. The best time to search is between 10am and 4pm on warm sunny days. Look on plant stems, on top of and underneath leaves (like nettles) and under tree bark.

A single 7-spot ladybird can eat 5000 aphids in its lifetime. Why do you think ladybirds are called the *gardener's friend*?

Ladybirds have a 4 step life cycle: egg, larva, pupa and adult.

Adult ladybirds are active from March to October. They hibernate in winter.

Many ladybirds are predatory, feeding on aphids (greenfly) or scale insects.

The harlequin ladybird is an invasive species. It is a very varied species, with more than 100 colour pattern varieties.

The harlequin ladybird arrived in Great Britain in 2004, when it was first found in Essex. By 2008 it had spread as far north as the Orkney Islands. Harlequins were first found in Ireland in 2010.

71. 7-spot ladybird

What to look for
Usually red with 7 spots. Black head with white patches in front corners.

Where to look
Lots of different plants. Stinging nettles are a good place to look.

When to see it
Adults active March to October. Adults found over- wintering in hollow stems at other times.

Date seen:

72. 2-spot ladybird

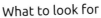

What to look for
Red with 2 spots: one on each side. To 6 mm long.

Where to look
Wide range of plants, including stinging nettle, sycamore and willow.

When to see it
April to October.

Date seen:

73. Harlequin (red)

What to look for

Large domed ladybird (to 8 mm long). Patterns very variable. Look for the white 'shoulders'. Mostly red.

Where to look

Wide range of plants, including stinging nettle, sycamore and willow.

When to see it

April to October, sometimes winter days.

Date seen:

74. Harlequin (black)

What to look for

Large domed ladybird (to 8 mm long). Patterns very variable. Look for the white 'shoulders'. Mostly black.

Where to look

Wide range of plants, including stinging nettle, sycamore and willow.

When to see it

April to October, sometimes winter days.

Date seen:

75. Ladybird larva

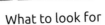

What to look for
A newly hatched ladybird does not look much like the adult. 6 legs. Long body divided into segments. Warts.

Where to look
Look on the underside of leaves like stinging nettles or sycamores.

When to see it
May to August.

Date seen:

76. Ladybird pupa

What to look for
The pupa is the stage where the larva changes into an adult. Dome shaped body with a hard outer covering.

Where to look
Look on the underside of leaves like stinging nettles or sycamores.

When to see it
May to August.

Date seen:

77. 14-spot ladybird

What to look for
Yellow-white body with between 4 and 14 black spots. Sometimes the spots are fused together.

Where to look
Look on the leaves and stems of garden shrubs such as roses. Less common in Scotland.

When to see it
May to September.

Date seen:

78. 22-spot ladybird

What to look for
Yellow body with 20-22 black spots. Each spot is roughly round in shape.

Where to look
Grassy places and hedgerows, particularly on hogweed. Less common north of Yorkshire.

When to see it
May to September.

Date seen:

79. Cream spot ladybird

What to look for
Orange-brown with 14 white or cream spots. Orange legs.

Where to look
Deciduous trees. Widespread throughout Great Britain and Ireland.

When to see it
Most active April to October.

Date seen:

80. Orange ladybird

What to look for
Orange with 12-16 white spots. Orange legs.

Where to look
Deciduous trees, especially ash and sycamore. Widespread England and Wales, less common Scotland and Ireland.

When to see it
Most active April to October.

Date seen:

Your record of Nature Spots

		Nature Spot				
Hedgerow birds	1	Robin				
	2	Blackbird				
	3	Song thrush				
	4	Wren				
	5	Chaffinch				
	6	Greenfinch				
	7	Long-tailed tit				
Hedgerow trees	8	Hawthorn				
	9	Blackthorn				
	10	Elder				
	11	Hazel				
	12	Holly				
	13	Field maple				
	14	Dog rose				
	15	Honeysuckle				
	16	Ivy				
	17	Bramble				
Wayside Flowers	18	Cow parsley				
	19	Greater stitchwort				
	20	Garlic mustard				
	21	Red campion				
	22	Foxglove				
	23	Rosebay willowherb				
	24	Greater willowherb				
	25	Red dead-nettle				
	26	White dead-nettle				
	27	Hedge woundwort				
	28	Hedge bindweed				
	29	Gorse				
	30	Broom				
	31	Bird's-foot trefoil				
	32	Primrose				
	33	Common vetch				
	34	Tufted vetch				
	35	Bittersweet				
	36	Scabious				
	37	Herb robert				
	38	Shining crane's-bill				
	39	Cut-leaved crane's-bill				
	40	Hedgerow crane's-bill				

		Nature Spot	🏅 🏅 🏅	✓
Marvellous mammels	41	Rabbit		
	42	Hare		
	43	Vole		
	44	Shrew		
	45	Mouse		
	46	Hedgehog		
	47	Fox		
	48	Badger		
	49	Deer		
	50	Stoat		
Signs of squirrels	51	Grey squirrel		
	52	Squirrel drey		
	53	Squirrel footprint		
	54	Stripped bark		
	55	Stripped pine cone		
	56	Nut eaten by squirrel		
	57	Nut eaten by mouse		
Mammal Tracks	58	Dog footprint		
	59	Fox footprint		
	60	Cat footprint		
Mammal Burrows	61	Mole hill		
	62	Rabbit hole		
	63	Fox earth		
	64	Badger sett		
	65	Badger hairs		
Mammal Droppings	66	Sheep droppings		
	67	Rabbit droppings		
	68	Deer droppings		
	69	Fox droppings		
	70	Badger droppings		
Looking for ladybirds	71	7-spot ladybird		
	72	2-spot ladybird		
	73	Harlequin (red)		
	74	Harlequin (black)		
	75	Ladybird larva		
	76	Ladybird pupa		
	77	14-spot ladybird		
	78	22-spot ladybird		
	79	Cream spot ladybird		
	80	Orange ladybird		

nature spotters

CERTIFICATE

of **Nature Spots** achieved

15 Nature Spots

Your signature: _____

Witnessed by: _____ Date: _____

30 Nature Spots

Your signature: _____

Witnessed by: _____ Date: _____

45 Nature Spots

Your signature: _____

Witnessed by: _____ Date: _____

60 Nature Spots

Your signature: _____

Witnessed by: _____ Date: _____

75 Nature Spots

Your signature: _____

Witnessed by: _____ Date: _____

CONGRATULATIONS!